I Am Canada

A Celebration

Text by
Heather Patterson

Illustrations by
Jeremy Tankard, Ruth Ohi,
Barbara Reid, Jon Klassen,
Marie-Louise Gay, Danielle Daniel,
Ashley Spires, Geneviève Côté,
Cale Atkinson, Doretta Groenendyk,
Qin Leng, Eva Campbell and
Irene Luxbacher

North Winds Press
An imprint of Scholastic Canada Ltd.

I am Canada.

I run, I swim,
I skate, I dance.

I skim over the snow
on my toboggan.

I have space.

I read, I learn,

I draw, I dream.

I stay out late and see the
northern lights.

I have time.

I watch, I touch, I listen.
I make up my mind.

I decide to build a castle.

I am free.
I am Canada.

I am cool in summer
and cozy in winter.

I am springy in the spring
and floppy in the fall.

I eat pizza and pierogis
and peppers.

I eat meatballs and muffins
and mangos.

I am quiet,

I am curious,

I am friendly,

I am funny.

I explain, I explore, I enjoy.
I share, I sing, I celebrate.

I am Canada.

We Are Canada

Heather Patterson
Author

I wrote this to invite Canadian children to celebrate our country's cultural diversity, and the diversity of our landscapes and seasons. I want them to celebrate their freedom to explore time and space, knowledge and beauty.

Jeremy Tankard
I am Canada.

I love that Canadians celebrate our diverse population as much as our varied landscape. This piece was an opportunity to celebrate both. I wanted an image that invites us into the book but also into the remarkable place we call home. And as a bonus I got to draw children hiking — one of my favourite activities!

Ruth Ohi
I run, I swim,
I skate, I dance.

Canada is about possibilities.
Dreams can come true here.

Barbara Reid
I skim over the snow on my toboggan.

Remember your very first toboggan ride? Watching news videos of Syrian kids newly arrived in Canada experiencing their first toboggan rides was my inspiration for this project. Their joy and delight was contagious. I couldn't stop smiling while making the picture!

Jon Klassen
I have space.

I live in California these days, and it has its charms for sure, but my illustration for this book contains a lot of things I miss. I miss elm trees and I miss blue shadows in winter and I miss how quiet new snow is and I miss Canada.

Marie-Louise Gay
I read, I learn,
I draw, I dream.

In these sometimes troubling and chaotic times, I think our hope lies with all the children of this country. That is why we must ensure that they have shelter, education and love so they can dream and imagine a luminous future for our country.

Danielle Daniel
I stay out late and see the northern lights.
I have time.

My work is deeply inspired by the lands, waters and forests that give life to our beautiful country. I am equally moved by the wildlife that populates our nation. Painting the northern lights that dance across our night skies is a love letter to my beloved Canada.

Ashley Spires
I watch, I touch, I listen.
I make up my mind.
I decide to build a castle.

Growing up on the coast of British Columbia, I had no idea why everyone said Canada was a cold place. I have since found out the truth, which is why I will never again move from my home near the beach in sunny South Delta.

Geneviève Côté
I am free. I am Canada.

After reading this, I started asking people: "How would you represent freedom?" and "What comes to mind when you think of Canada?" There were lively conversations, recurring themes — space, open skies, movement, distant horizons — and one common stance: arms open wide, head high, ready to fly!

Cale Atkinson
I am cool in summer and cozy in winter.
I am springy in the spring and floppy in the fall.

I am proud to call myself Canadian and feel lucky to be part of a project that brings together so much of the fantastic talent our fair land has to offer. Canada is many things to many people; for me, it is home. Now please pass the maple syrup.

Doretta Groenendyk
I eat pizza and pierogis and peppers.
I eat meatballs and muffins and mangos.

Painting a midnight feast for *I Am Canada* filled me with glee (and made me hungry)! Across Canada, communities share food, stories and culture. My family is always happy to join in a local potluck!

Qin Leng

I am quiet, I am curious,
I am friendly, I am funny.

My family moved to Canada in September 1991, and I remember vividly our weekend hikes on Mount Royal, jumping into piles of vibrant red, yellow and orange leaves, and feeding a squirrel for the first time. When I read the poem, the woods of Mount Royal on a beautiful fall morning is what came to my mind.

Eva Campbell

I explain, I explore, I enjoy.
I share, I sing, I celebrate.

I was excited about this project because it made me think about what *I Am Canada* means in a fun and playful way — depicting activities children might do as they live, learn and celebrate!

Irene Luxbacher

I am Canada.

My parents immigrated to Canada in the 1960s, so I've hardly begun to unpack my suitcase of family stories . . . As I do so, I hope it's with a deep respect and awareness of the wild integrity of this country's landscape, its Indigenous people and its soul-searching pioneers.

Library and Archives Canada Cataloguing in Publication

Patterson, Heather, 1945-, author
I am Canada : a celebration / Heather Patterson ; illustrated
by Barbara Reid [and 12 others].

ISBN 978-1-4431-6304-0 (hardcover)

1. Canada--Pictorial works--Juvenile literature. 2. Children--
Canada--Pictorial works--Juvenile literature. 3. National
characteristics, Canadian--Juvenile literature. I. Reid, Barbara,
1957-, illustrator II. Title.

FC58.P38 2017   j971.0022'2   C2017-900228-7

www.scholastic.ca

Photo credits: Eva Campbell by Danielle Pope; Danielle Daniel by Gerry Kingsley;
Doretta Groenendyk by Dennis Robinson; Jon Klassen by Moranne Keeler;
Ruth Ohi by Annie T.; Barbara Reid by Ian Crysler.
Image at bottom right of cover: Logorilla/iStockphoto.

6 5 4 3 2 1   Printed in Canada 114   17 18 19 20 21

FSC
www.fsc.org

MIX
Paper from
responsible sources
FSC® C016245